TANTRI AND THE SINGER

Writer: Anomita Guha
Illustrations: Prachi Killekar
Colouring: Umesh Sarode

AAAAEEEIO!

WHAT'S THAT AWFUL NOISE?!

IT SOUNDS LIKE TWELVE HUNDRED CATS YOWLING AND FIGHTING!

OR SOMEONE BEING HORRIBLY TORTURED! OH, MY POOR EARS!

AAAEEEEIO!

HOOJA! YOU'RE THE ONE BEHIND THIS CACOPHONY…ER, I MEAN, THIS MELODIOUS PERFORMANCE?!

I'M TAKING SINGING LESSONS! DON'T I SOUND GOOD?

ER…YES…JUST LIKE A NIGHTINGALE…

…WITH A SORE THROAT!

AS SOON AS I FINISH LEARNING THIS RAAG, I'M GOING TO HAVE A PRIVATE CONCERT JUST FOR YOU, TANTRI!

GULP! LUCKY ME!

I'D BETTER FIND SOME COTTON WOOL TO STUFF INTO MY EARS!

LATER –

DUSHTABUDDHI, YOU MUST INVENT A NEW DEVICE TO GET RID OF HOOJA AT ONCE! HE KEEPS THREATENING TO SING TO ME AND THAT'S A FATE WORSE THAN DEATH!

CALM DOWN, TANTRI! I HAVE JUST THE THING!

A SITAR? DON'T TELL ME YOU'VE BECOME A MUSIC LOVER TOO!

NO...NO... THIS IS A DEADLY DEVICE I'VE JUST INVENTED!

WHEN HOOJA STRUMS THIS INNOCENT-LOOKING SITAR, IT WILL ACTIVATE A DEVICE...

...THAT WILL CAUSE A BOMB CONCEALED IN THE SITAR TO EXPLODE THE MOMENT HOOJA SINGS A HIGH NOTE!

DUSHTA, YOU'VE OUTDONE YOURSELF!

THE NEXT DAY –

YOUR ROYAL CHUBBINESS, ER, MAJESTY...I HAVE A SMALL GIFT FOR YOU!

OH, TANTRI! A NEW SITAR! COME, I'LL SING A SONG FOR YOU RIGHT NOW!

NO! DON'T DO THAT! YOU SHOULD MAKE SURE THAT YOU'RE COMFORTABLE WITH IT FIRST. WHY DON'T YOU PRACTICE ON IT TONIGHT WHEN YOU REHEARSE YOUR SINGING?

HMM...GOOD IDEA! I'LL DO AS YOU SAY, MY DEAR TANTRI!

WHEW! THAT WAS A CLOSE CALL! I'LL HIDE OUTSIDE HOOJA'S BEDROOM TONIGHT TO MAKE SURE THAT THE SITAR BOMB GOES OFF!

2

THAT NIGHT –

TANTRI IS SO THOUGHTFUL! HE'S ALWAYS ENCOURAGING ME TO PURSUE MY TALENTS!

PLINK, PLINK

HOOJA HAS SET OFF THE BOMB'S TIMER! NOW WHEN HE HITS THE HIGH NOTE, HE'LL SING HIS OWN SWAN SONG!

BUT...

AAA...

THUD!

...AN ASSASSIN SENT BY RAJA DOOJA MAKES HIS ENTRY AT THAT MOMENT.

HE'S OUT COLD!

W...WHAT'S GOING ON IN THERE? WHY ISN'T HOOJA SINGING?!

RAJA HOOJA! WE ARE WAITING TO HEAR YOUR EXQUISITE VOICE! PLEASE DO SING US YOUR FAVOURITE RAAG!

ULP! THEY'RE EXPECTING HIM TO SING!

AAAAAIII...

MARVELLOUS, SIRE!

STRANGE! HOOJA ACTUALLY SOUNDS BETTER THAN HE DID BEFORE!

...EEEEEOOO!

HE HIT THE HIGH NOTE!

BOOM

IT WORKED! HE'S GONE AND I'M FINALLY...

TANTRI! WHAT'S GOING ON?! I FEEL DAZED...WHAT WAS THAT LOUD NOISE ?!

GASP!

WHO'S THAT MAN? DID HE COME HERE TO ATTACK ME?! DID YOU SET OFF AN EXPLOSION TO STOP HIM, TANTRI?!

(GROAN)... YES, I...I DID!

YOU'VE SAVED ME YET AGAIN, MY FRIEND! I MUST REWARD YOUR CLEVERNESS BY SINGING A SPECIAL RAGA JUST FOR YOU!

SOB!

TANTRI THE MANTRI
SPECIAL EFFECTS

Illustrations : Prachi Killekar

TANTRI WAS VISITING A PALMIST.

CACKLE! I CAN SEE A CROWN ON YOUR HEAD. SOON. VERY SOON.

THAT MEANS I WILL BE KING!

TANTRI'S MIND WAS IN A WHIRL.

IT IS DESTINED THAT I WILL BE KING. SO I DON'T NEED TO PLOT. A PLOT WILL COME TO ME.

ASTRO THE PALMIST

AND SURE ENOUGH, A FEW DAYS LATER, TANTRI HAD A VISITOR.

HO HUM... NEXT.

I AM CHATURAMANI, MASTER SCULPTOR. MY SPECIALITY IS MAKING SCULPTURES LARGER THAN LIFE...

BUT THE MAN DRONED ON —

... OF UNBREAKABLE MATERIAL WITH MOVABLE PARTS WHICH CAN RAISE AN ARM IN SALUTE, BOW A HEAD IN OBEISANCE*...

STOP! CAN YOUR STATUES FALL FLAT ON THE GROUND?

IT IS DESTINY! THE PLOT HAS COME TO ME.

CHATURAMANI HESITATED —

I'VE NEVER HAD AN ORDER LIKE THAT. I'M NOT SURE ....

HE'S BACKING OUT. MUST STOP HIM.

5

THE STATUE IS A GIFT FOR OUR BELOVED KING RAJA HOOJA. HE LOVES SPECIAL EFFECTS. THE WHACKIER, THE BETTER. HE'LL PAY YOU DOUBLE WHEN HE SEES THE STATUE DOESN'T HAVE A CRACK ON IT AFTER CRASHING.

STRANGE FELLOWS, THESE NOBLES. BUT I'M NOT ARGUING WHEN THERE'S MORE MONEY.

WHEW! THAT WAS CLOSE

NOW, YOU MUST MAKE A STATUE OF KING HOOJA. IT MUST COME CRASHING DOWN WHEN HE UNVEILS IT ON HIS BIRTHDAY

I'LL START RIGHT AWAY.

THE STATUE WAS SOON COMPLETED.

EXCELLENT!

JUST ONE MORE DETAIL.

THERE.

THE FINISHING TOUCH. MARVELLOUS!

TANTRI HANDED OVER THE MONEY.

THANK YOU. JUST MAKE SURE NO ONE IS UNDER THE STATUE, WHEN IT FALLS. HA! HA!

HA! HA! OF COURSE!

NO ONE BUT HOOJA, HEH HEH!

ON THE DAY OF THE UNVEILING TANTRI ESCORTED A SPECIAL GUEST TO THE SEAT BESIDE HOOJA.

THIS IS ASTRO, THE GREAT PALMIST, RAJA HOOJA.

OOH! I LOVE FORTUNE-TELLERS.

AS TANTRI BUSIED HIMSELF WITH THE PREPARATIONS —

WILL YOU READ MY PALM, ASTRO?

WITH PLEASURE, YOUR MAJESTY.

OH OH! I SEE GREAT DANGER FOR YOU.. SOON. VERY SOON. DO NOT MOVE FROM YOUR SEAT.

BUT... BUT....

MOVE AND YOU ARE DEAD!

GULP! ALL RIGHT.

JUST THEN TANTRI CAME UP.

YOUR MAJESTY, IT IS TIME FOR THE UNVEILING.

AH ... OH... ER...TANTRI, I HAVE AN IDEA. YOU DO THE UNVEILING.

ME!? BUT....

NO BUTS. THIS IS HIS MAJESTY'S ORDER.

GO ON, HURRY UP!

ASTRO HANDED THE ROPE TO TANTRI.

LET THE UNVEILING BEGIN.

TANTRI PULLED THE ROPE.

SIGH! ANOTHER FAILED PLOT.

CRASH

GOODNESS ME, ASTRO! YOU WERE RIGHT!

PLONK

HE ALWAYS IS, YOUR MAJESTY.

TANTRI THE MANTRI

BALLET BUNGLE

Illustrations :
Prachi Killekar

RUSSIAN BALLERINA, KATERINA, WAS VISITING RAJA HOOJA'S KINGDOM.

SHE'S BEAUTIFUL!

WHAT GRACE! WHAT POISE!

AFTER THE PERFORMANCE —

TANTRI, I MUST CONFESS, IT HAS LONG BEEN MY DESIRE TO LEARN HOW TO DANCE.

!?!

HELLO, KING HOOJA, HOPE YOU ENJOYED THE PERFORMANCE.

IT WAS BRILLIANT!

ER.... MY MINISTER CAME UP WITH A GOOD IDEA THIS MORNING. HE SAID WE SHOULD LEARN TO DANCE.

DID I ?

THE BALLERINA WAS TAKEN ABACK AND SO WAS TANTRI.

YOU WANT TO LEARN BALLET ?

YES! YES!

THIS PUDDING? HE WILL LOOK LIKE AN ELEPHANT IN BALLET SHOES! BUT AFTER ALL HE IS THE KING.

SO —

OKAY. WE'LL START YOUR LESSONS IN THE PALACE HALL TOMORROW.

YIPPEE!

THAT NIGHT TANTRI SAT UP THINKING.

THE FATSO! DRAGGING ME ALONG AND SAYING THAT BALLET LESSONS WERE MY IDEA!

BUT IT COULD BE FUN TOO.

THE NEXT DAY TANTRI SET OFF EARLY.

WAX

SCRUB A DUB-DUB I'LL BEAT HIM WITH A CLUB. SCRUB A DUB-DOO I'LL TRIP HIM WITH MY SHOE.

SCRUB A DUB-DEE HE'LL SLIP AND BREAK HIS KNEE.

IT IS SLIPPERY.

THAT EVENING —

HA! HA! TANTRI, SKINNY LEGS, BONY BOY!

WHAT ABOUT YOU...YOU TURKEY!

THE BALLERINA WAS WAITING FOR THEM.

THIS IS NOT GOING TO BE EASY.

LET'S BEGIN. I MUST SAY YOUR BALLROOM IS EXQUISITE.

I HAD IT WAXED ESPECIALLY FOR HIS MAJESTY.

AND GREASED TOO! HA! HA!

REMEMBER, BALLET IS ALL ABOUT POISE. IT IS ABOUT GETTING YOUR FOOTWORK RIGHT. WE MUST GET YOU PROPER FOOTWEAR.

BUT WHEN THEY TRIED —

HA! HA! HO! HO! HA! HA!

DON'T BE DISHEARTENED.. WE'LL DO A JETE* NOW.

* A JETE IS A JUMP IN BALLET FROM BOTH FEET TO ONE FOOT.

BUT HOOJA DID NOT WANT TO BE LAUGHED AT AGAIN. SO —

PUFF...PUFF.... PANT...PANT... LET TANTRI DO IT FIRST.

AND BEFORE TANTRI COULD REFUSE —

GO ON TO THE FLOOR. RUN A BIT AND LEAP UP INTO THE AIR.

BUT .. BUT.....

AS HE DID NOT HAVE SPECIAL SHOES LIKE THE BALLERINA —

OH !

AH !

OOOH !

OH DEAR ! POOR TANTRI !

WHAT DRAMA ! WHAT STYLE ! SPLENDID !

CRASH

A PERFECT JUMP, TANTRI! NOW LET'S PRACTISE THE LANDING.

12

TANTRI THE MANTRI

The Apple Twist

Based on story sent by:
S. N. Pratap Sinha,

Illustrations : Prachi Killekar

TANTRI WAS TIRED OF WAITING IN THE WINGS.

HOW LONG HAVE I WAITED FOR RAJA HOOJA TO DISAPPEAR SO I CAN BE KING. WHY, I'VE LOST COUNT OF THE YEARS!

AN APPLE A DAY KEEPS THE DOCTOR AWAY, TANTRI. HERE HAVE ONE !

BAH!

WHAT ?

I MEAN, GREAT! WHAT A GOOD HEALTH TIP !

TANTRI CHOMPED ON THE ROSY APPLE WITH MURDER IN HIS HEART.

HOW I WISH AN APPLE ONE DAY WOULD SEND YOU AWAY – FOREVER!

SUDDENLY HE BRIGHTENED UP.

WOW! WHAT AN IDEA ! I'M SO CLEVER.

THAT YOU ARE ! BUT WHAT'S THE IDEA?

I'LL LET YOU KNOW, IN GOOD TIME.

HE RAN TO THE HOUSE OF HIS FRIEND, CHATURBUDDHI.

I'VE BROUGHT FRUITS FOR YOU.

HOW SWEET ! THOUGH MY IDEAS HAVEN'T BEEN VERY FRUITFUL SO FAR.

BUT NOW THEY WILL. TAKE THE STRONGEST POISON, THE FASTEST POISON YOU KNOW.

AND ?

THEN, WITH A SYRINGE INJECT IT INTO THE APPLES.

OH ! POISON-INJECTED APPLES. A CLEVER RUSE !

TAKE CARE THAT THERE ARE NO MARKS. USE THE FINEST NEEDLE.

RIGHT ! SO TELL ME WHICH POISON WILL WORK IN TINY DOSES?

TANTRI'S FAVOURITE BEDTIME STORIES WERE MYSTERIES AND THRILLERS. SO HE HAD A QUICK REPLY.

SKYCHRINE.

RIGHT ! YOUR WORK WILL BE DONE.

TANTRI SLEPT FITFULLY THAT NIGHT.

14

AS HE LAUGHED ALOUD IN HIS DREAM, HE FELL OFF HIS BED AND WOKE UP WITH A START.

HUH? OH! AT LEAST IN MY DREAM I WAS CROWNED KING. NOW TO MAKE THE DREAM COME TRUE.

CHATURBUDDHI HAD BEEN BUSY TOO. HE DID NOT WANT TO FORGET THE NAME OF THE POISON. SO -

SKYCHRINE SKYCHRINE SKYCHRINE

BUT A SMALL ROCK TRIPPED HIM.

THUD

CHATURBUDDHI'S FALL MADE HIM FORGET THE NAME HE HAD BEEN MEMORISING. HE REACHED THE CHEMIST'S SHOP QUITE CONFUSED.

I WANT STRYCHMA NO---NO- SAM CINE - NO---NO-NO- SOLUCINE.

OH DEAR! WHO IS IT FOR? CAN'T YOU REMEMBER ANYTHING?

IT'S FOR RAJA HOOJA. TANTRI HAD ASKED FOR IT!

OHH! THEN IT MUST BE SACCHARIN*. TANTRI IS VERY CONCERNED ABOUT HOOJA'S WEIGHT.

LATER –

HERE ARE THE APPLES FULL OF THE S-S- SPECIAL JUICE.

* A SWEETENER USED IN PLACE OF SUGAR

TANTRI TOOK THE APPLES AND PUT THEM BY THE ROYAL BED.

YAWN! I THINK I'LL TURN IN EARLY TONIGHT.

DON'T FORGET YOUR APPLES, YOUR MAJESTY.

YOU ARE SO CONCERNED ABOUT MY HEALTH.

YOUR WEALTH ACTUALLY.

RAJA MUNCHED AWAY AT THE APPLES.

THEY ARE STRANGELY SWEET.

HMM! BITTER SWEET.

THE HARMLESS SYNTHETIC SWEETENER MADE THE APPLES TASTE DIFFERENT.

TANTRI WAITED ALL NIGHT BY THE BEDSTEAD AND CHECKED THE KING'S PULSE AND BREATH EVERY HOUR.

DRAT! BREATHING LIKE A BABOON!

NEXT MORNING —

GOOD MORNING! GOOD MORNING, TANTRI! I SEE YOU'VE BEEN WATCHING OVER ME LIKE A GUARDIAN ANGEL.

GRR! WHEN ALL I WANT TO BE IS A NASTY DEVIL.

TANTRI THE MANTRI
THE TANTRI MACHINE

ILLUSTRATIONS : PRACHI KILLEKAR

TANTRI WAS AS GLUM AS A DARK CLOUD.

POISON, BOMBS, TRAPS ! NOTHING HAS WORKED SO FAR. BUT DON'T GIVE UP TANTRI, HANG ON !

JUST THEN, IN CAME DUSHTABUDDHI.

AH, DUSHTABUDDHI ! THE LIGHT IN MY TUNNEL. WHAT HAVE YOU BROUGHT FOR ME?

SOMETHING VERY SPECIAL, TANTRI. JUST LOOK AT THIS.

HE UNCOVERED THE HIDDEN OBJECT AND —

GAWK ! WHAT IS THIS?

IT IS OOLA, A ROBOT THAT LOOKS EXACTLY LIKE YOU. IT HAS BEEN PROGRAMMED TO TAKE ORDERS FROM NO ONE BUT YOU, TANTRI.

TANTRI DECIDED TO TRY OUT THE ROBOT.

OOLA, BRING ME AN APPLE FROM THE GARDEN.

IN OOLA'S HEAD —

<< WHRRRR>> <<VOICE OF MASTER SPEAKING>> <<MASTER WISHES TO HAVE AN APPLE>> <<APPLE IS IN THE GARDEN>>

WITHIN SECONDS —

HERE, MASTER. AN APPLE FOR YOU.

GOOD, OOLA.

OOLA IS WONDERFUL, DUSHTABUDDHI. NOW I CAN GET HIM TO DO MY DIRTY WORK. HEE HEE!

HEE HEE! NOW YOU WILL NOT FAIL.

DUSHTABUDDHI LEFT THE ROOM WITH A BAG FULL OF GOLD COINS.

TANTRI WAS VERY PLEASED WITH HIS NEW MACHINE.

A COMPUTER CAN NEVER GO WRONG. THIS TIME HOOJA HAS HAD IT!

OOLA, AFTER YOU FINISH SWEEPING THE FLOOR, COME HERE AND SIT WITH ME. WE MUST TALK!

YES, MASTER.

SO —

LISTEN ... TAKE RAJA HOOJA FOR A WALK...BY A CLIFF...WHEN HE IS THERE PUSH HIM DOWN....

<<MASTER'S VOICE>> <<WHRRR>> <<HOOJA>> <<FOR A WALK>> <<CLIFF>> <<PUSH HIM DOWN>> << WHRR>> <<CLICK>>

THAT EVENING —

OOLA, THAT IS RAJA HOOJA. DO YOU REMEMBER THE PLAN? DON'T DISAPPOINT ME. GO!

<<WHRRR>> <<CLICK>> YES, MASTER.

HELLO, YOUR MAJESTY.

HELLO, HELLO, TANTRI! COME

BUT ON HEARING HOOJA'S VOICE —

<<WHRRR>> <<SIT DOWN>> <<NOT MASTER'S VOICE>> <<REJECT COMMAND>> <<WHRRR>>

NO, I WON'T SIT, YOUR MAJESTY.

HUH?

LET'S TAKE A WALK. <<WHRRR>>

TANTRI IS BEING STRANGE.

OKAY, TANTRI. BUT WHAT IS THAT WHIRRING NOISE EVERY TIME YOU SPEAK?

OOLA LED THE WAY AS HAD BEEN INSTRUCTED BY TANTRI.

YOUR MAJESTY, COME THIS WAY. <<WHRRR>>

HUH! OKAY, TANTRI.

TANTRI SEEMS TO HAVE A BAD STOMACH. IT'S WHIRRING TOO MUCH. I MUST TRY CHEER HIM UP.

WHILE HOOJA WAS THINKING OF SOMETHING FUNNY TO SAY, OOLA HAD ONLY ONE GOAL IN MIND.

TO THE CLIFF <<WHRRR>> DOWN THE CLIFF <<WHRRR>>

I HAVE JOINED A MIMICRY CLASS, TANTRI.

MEANWHILE TANTRI WAS WATCHING FROM A DISTANCE.

VERY GOOD, OOLA. JUST TEN STEPS MORE AND I WILL BE KING! HE HE HE!

RAJA HOOJA BEGAN TELLING OOLA ALL ABOUT HIS MIMICRY CLASS.

WHEN THEY TOLD US TO BE A FROG, I LET OUT THE BIGGEST CROAK. I SAID, 'CROAK'!

HE TAUGHT ME HOW TO SPEAK IN YOUR VOICE TOO, TANTRI . LISTEN TO THIS - "HELLO, I AM TANTRI."

<<WHRRRR>>??? <<MASTER'S VOICE>>

HOOJA WENT ON IN TANTRI'S VOICE WITH A POEM HE HAD LEARNT.

♪ IF YOU WANT TO PLAY ♪ IF YOU WANT SOME FUN, BRING ME THAT BRIGHT BALL ♪ THE ORANGE SUN. ♪

AT ONCE IN OOLA'S HEAD —

<<WHRRR>> <<CHANGE OF ORDERS>><<NO CLIFF>> MASTER WANTS THE SUN. GET MASTER THE SUN.

OOLA RUSHED IN THE DIRECTION OF THE SUN.

AND —

CRASH

OH NO ! TANTRI, WHY DID YOU JUMP ? WHAT DROVE YOU TO TAKE THIS DRASTIC STEP ! SNIFF !

OH NO ! OOLA !!!

TANTRI! YOU'RE HERE? HOW IS IT POSSIBLE? YOU HAVE LEARNT THE DISAPPEARING TRICK, HAVEN'T YOU? COME, JUMP AND DEMOSTRATE IT AGAIN !

BAH !

TANTRI THE MANTRI
IN
THE CRUNCHY CAPTURE

Based on a story sent by:
K. Aashish Naidu,

Illustrations : Prachi Killekar

IT HAD BEEN A PEACEFUL NIGHT AND DAWN WAS JUST BREAKING, WHEN —

CLANG! CLANG!

RAISE THE ALARM! THE NOTORIOUS BANDIT, BANDOOK RAM HAS ESCAPED! RAISE THE ALARM....

AND NOW TO SETTLE MY SCORES WITH HOOJA ! I HAVE SPENT SO MANY DAYS IN PRISON BECAUSE OF HIM.

AT THE PALACE —

GUARDS ! WHAT IS ALL THIS COMMOTION? WHAT IS HAPPENING?

THE DREADED BANDOOK RAM HAS ESCAPED FROM PRISON, SIRE. WE ARE POSTING EXTRA GUARDS FOR YOUR PROTECTION.

MEANWHILE TANTRI WAS DREAMING.

WAKE UP, TANTRI , WAKE UP! IT IS TIME FOR YOU TO BE KING. WAKE UP AND SALUTE MY INTELLIGENCE. WAKE UP ! COME ON, WAKE UP-P-P-P !

AAH! HELP - P! COUGH....

WAKE UP! WAKE UP!

DUSHTABUDDHI, WHAT ARE YOU DOING HERE?

I AM HERE TO SHOW YOU ...

... MY GREATEST INVENTION! TA...DA-A-A!

AN APPLE!?

JUST HOW MANY TIMES DO I TELL THIS FOOL? AN APPLE WILL KEEP HOOJA AWAY FROM THE ROYAL DOCTORS. I WANT HIM TO GO TO THE ROYAL HOSPITAL AND STAY THERE, FOREVER!

DON'T UNDERESTIMATE THIS APPLE. JUST ONE BITE CAN KNOCK YOU OUT FOR A WEEK. IF YOU EAT IT ALL, IT WILL KILL YOU.

HMM ... REALLY?!

YES! IT CONTAINS THE WORLD'S DEADLIEST POISONS AND TOXINS. AND IT CAN BE YOURS FOR JUST FIVE THOUSAND GOLD COINS.

THAT WAS A STEEP PRICE TO PAY FOR AN APPLE. BUT STILL ... NOW TO GET PUDDING FACE TO EAT IT .. HMM... BUT HOW... I GET IT. I'LL GO TO THE MARKET AND GET A....

SO, AFTER A HURRIED VISIT TO THE MARKET, TANTRI WAS ALL SET.

THERE! I'LL RECOGNIZE THE POISON APPLE NOW. IT IS THE BIGGEST OF THE LOT. NOW I CAN BE SURE THAT IT IS JELLY BELLY HOOJA AND NOT ME WHO WILL GET KNOCKED OUT.

AT THE PALACE —

GREETINGS, SIRE!

TANTRI, COME JOIN ME FOR BREAKFAST. I SEE YOU COME BEARING A GIFT FOR ME AS USUAL.

NO THANKS, SIRE. I HAVE JUST HAD BREAKFAST.

OH, COME ON, TANTRI... CRUNCH... HMM..HERE JUST ONE APPLE... FRESH FROM THE BASKET YOU JUST BROUGHT ...HMM... GO AHEAD, THEY ARE DELICIOUS.

JUST MY LUCK THAT HE PICKED THE POISONOUS ONE FOR ME. WHY COULDN'T HE HAVE EATEN IT? BUT WELL, AT LEAST, I AM PREPARED THIS TIME.

ER..NO..SIRE.. IT IS THE LARGEST APPLE OF THE LOT. SO ONLY YOU SHOULD HAVE IT.

AH, TANTRI! LOYAL AS EVER! BUT SINCE YOU ARE SO CLOSE TO ME, I INSIST YOU HAVE IT.

NO, SIRE... PLEASE ....

COME ON, TANTRI ... I INSIST!

OH, OKAY! HAVE THIS ONE THEN.

PHEW!

SUDDENLY, TANTRI HAD A BRIGHT IDEA AND —

TANTRI! WHY DID YOU THROW THAT APPLE OUT OF THE WINDOW?

ER..SIRE..I JUST ..ER..NOTICED THAT ..ER.. IT HAD BEEN INFESTED WITH WORMS.

ALL THIS WHILE, IN THE PALACE GARDENS —

LOOK! THERE IS BANDOOK RAM. HE IS GOING TO CLIMB INTO THE KING'S CHAMBERS THROUGH THAT WINDOW.

WE MUST STOP HIM! BUT HOW?

JUST THEN —

THUNK!

!?

HUH! WHAT IS THIS? WHERE DID THIS COME FROM? AH WELL, I'LL EAT IT ANYWAY.

BANDOOK RAM TOOK ONE BITE OF THE APPLE AND FELL UNCONSCIOUS.

HE'S FAINTING! QUICK! CAPTURE HIM! I'LL GO INFORM RAJA HOOJA!

THE GUARD RUSHED TO HOOJA AND GAVE HIM THE NEWS.

LOOK TANTRI! IT IS THE SAME APPLE THAT YOU THREW OUT! GOSH, I WONDER HOW MANY WORMS IT CONTAINED.

COME ON, TANTRI, LET'S CELEBRATE. AN APPLE, PERHAPS?

!

TANTRI THE MANTRI

DOOJA'S MASTER PLAN

Based on a story sent by:
K. Indrajeet and Ranjeet,

Illustrations :
Prachi Killekar

HOOJA WAS LEAVING FOR A ONE-MONTH HEALTH PROGRAMME.

FAREWELL, TANTRI. TAKE GOOD CARE OF THE KINGDOM IN MY ABSENCE.

YES, SIRE. DON'T... ER...DO COME BACK SOON.

OF COURSE, TANTRI. IN A MONTH YOU WILL SEE A SLIMMER, FITTER ME.

OR BETTER STILL, I MAY NEVER SEE YOU AGAIN. THE BOAT MIGHT SINK OR YOU MAY HAVE AN ACCIDENT AT THE HEALTH RESORT.

PUT PUT CHUG

THE VERY NEXT DAY, TANTRI CALLED THE GREAT MINDS OF DESTRUCTION, DUSHTABUDDHI AND KUBUDDHI.

WE HAVE ONE FULL MONTH TO MAKE A PLAN AND FINISH OFF HOOJA WHEN HE COMES BACK.

THE BRAINSTORMING SESSION BEGAN.

....POISONED APPLES OR A SPECIAL BOMB...

...A KILLER FLOWER...ITCHY CLOTHES.

TRIED AND FAILED... TRIED AND FAILED!

CAN'T YOU THINK OF SOMETHING ELSE?

CAN'T HE THINK OF SOMETHING ELSE OTHER THAN FINISHING OFF HOOJA?

NO MORE OF YOUR COMPLEX PLOTS. I AM GOING TO TRY SOMETHING SIMPLE THIS TIME. PLEASE LEAVE.

HRUMPH!

AND NOT VERY FAR AWAY, IN RAJA DOOJA'S KINGDOM —

IT IS ALWAYS TANTRI WHO FOILS ALL OUR PLANS TO GET RID OF HOOJA.

HMM...WE MUST GET RID OF HIM FIRST. BUT HOW?

HOOJA IS AWAY FOR A MONTH. I HAVE THOUGHT OF A BRILLIANT PLAN! LISTEN... BZZ BZZ....

TWO WEEKS LATER —

TANTRI, MY MANTRI!

THAT SOUNDS LIKE FAT FACE.

AND SO IT WAS —

W...WEREN'T YOU SUPPOSED TO COME AFTER A MONTH?

YES, BUT I MISSED YOU SO MUCH!

HOW DID YOU LOSE SO MUCH WEIGHT IN JUST TWO WEEKS?

ER...THE WONDERS OF A CRASH DIET, EH?

THE VERY NEXT DAY TANTRI DECIDED TO PUT HIS 'SIMPLE' PLAN INTO ACTION.

YOUR HIGHNESS WHY DON'T WE....

MANTRI...ER...TANTRI, I WAS THINKING...WE SHOULD GO ON A DAY'S PICNIC. THEN I CAN CATCH UP WITH ALL I HAVE MISSED.

THAT WAS EXACTLY WHAT I WAS GOING TO SUGGEST, YOUR HIGHNESS.

HEH HEH! GREAT MINDS THINK ALIKE. ANYWAY, LET'S GO TO SOME NICE, COOL HIGH MOUNTAIN RANGE OVERLOOKING A VALLEY.

TANTRI COULD HARDLY BELIEVE HIS EARS.

YES, YES! A TALL MOUNTAIN RANGE OVERLOOKING A DEEP DARK VALLEY. I KNOW JUST THE ONE.

LET'S GO!

AS THEY TREKKED UP THE MOUNTAINS —

HURRY UP, SLOWPOKE!

HUFF.. FAT FACE HAS REALLY BECOME FITTER..PUFF.

QUITE A DROP, EH?

HEH HEH! SHALL WE HAVE A SNACK?

YOU'LL KNOW WHEN I PUSH YOU DOWN!

DO HAVE A JALEBI, SIRE.

YECH! I MEAN, I HAVE GIVEN UP EATING JALEBIS.

NO, NO. I HAVE GIVEN UP SWEETS. TO MAINTAIN MY HEALTH, MANTRI... ER... TANTRI.

THEN AT LEAST HAVE SOME LADOOS.

DRAT! THERE GOES PART ONE OF MY PLAN. FAT FACE WAS TO EAT THESE POISONED SWEETS BEFORE I THREW HIM OFF THE MOUNTAIN... TCH!

SUDDENLY —

TANTRI!

HUH?

W... WHO ARE YOU?

THAT'S AN IMPOSTOR, TANTRI! I AM THE REAL HOOJA. HE HAS BEEN SENT BY DOOJA TO KILL YOU!

ME, AN IMPOSTOR? HOW DARE YOU!

SENT TO KILL ME?

I HEARD EVERYTHING, YOU CHEAT! YOU CLAIM TO BE ME AND DON'T EVEN EAT SWEETS?

I WAS JUST...DON'T BELIEVE HIM, MANTRI... ER... TANTRI.

WHAT IS HAPPENING?

AND JUST LOOK AT HIM, TANTRI. HE IS ALL SKIN AND BONES... WILL I EVER BE SO THIN?

WONDERS OF A C... CRASH DIET, MANTRI. DON'T BELIEVE HIM.

STOP IT! WHO IS THE REAL RAJA HOOJA?

NOT YOU, MR SKINNY!

I AM!

PROVE IT.

YES, PROVE IT AND BE QUICK!

I HAVE TO THROW ONE OF YOU DOWN THE VALLEY.

THE THINNER 'HOOJA' POPPED A LADOO IN HIS MOUTH AND —

SEE...MUNCH I DO LIKE SWEETS....

SWOON

SEE? I'M SURE HE POISONED THOSE LADOOS.

BUT HOW DID YOU...?

I HEARD OF DOOJA'S CONSPIRACY AND RUSHED TO SAVE YOU, MY DEAREST FRIEND!

AND SAVED YOURSELF TOO! I SHOULD HAVE MADE YOU EAT A LADOO AS WELL.

TANTRI THE MANTRI

Say Cheese!

Illustrations:
Prachi Killekar

HOKI POKI WAS VERY WORRIED.

YOU DON'T EAT WELL, YOU KEEP MUTTERING TO YOURSELF AND LOOK AT YOUR EYES! WHAT IS THE MATTER WITH YOU?

N...NOTHING. JUST WORK AND THE KINGDOM...

...THAT I WANT TO BE KING OF.

SOON —

I WAS TALKING TO HOKI YESTERDAY, TANTRI. SHE IS RIGHT. YOU NEED A CHANGE. WHY DON'T WE GO ON A SHORT HOLIDAY?

SURE, SURE. YOU CAN GO ON A HOLIDAY, YOUR HIGHNESS. I WILL RULE...ER...MANAGE THE KINGDOM.

NO, NO. I MEANT FOR BOTH OF US TO GO ON A HOLIDAY. WHY DON'T WE GO TO GOA? THE SUN, THE SAND AND THE SEA WILL SURELY CHEER YOU UP!

HMM.

FAT FACE COULD DROWN IN THE SEA, SINK IN QUICKSAND... THE POSSIBILITIES ARE ENDLESS!

THE VERY NEXT DAY THEY WERE IN GOA.

THE SEA LOOKS LOVELY, DOESN'T IT? CAN YOU SWIM, YOUR HIGHNESS?

NO, TANTRI. BUT I'D LIKE TO LEARN.

LATE THAT NIGHT —

I NEED A FAULTY LIFE JACKET. IT SHOULD SINK IN WATER WHEN WORN.

SURE.

THE NEXT MORNING –

LET'S LEARN SWIMMING TODAY. I HAVE ALREADY ARRANGED FOR LIFE JACKETS AND AN INSTRUCTOR.

OKAY.

WHY ARE WE STANDING ON A CLIFF TO LEARN SWIMMING, TANTRI?

ER...SO WE CAN LEARN DIVING TOO. THE INSTRUCTOR SHOULD BE HERE IN A WHILE.

INSTRUCTOR? HEH HEH! I'LL JUST PUSH YOU INTO THE WATER AND WATCH YOU DROWN.

THIS IS A VERY NICE LIFE JACKET, TANTRI. IT DOES SUIT MY PERSONALITY, DON'T YOU THINK?

UH OH! I AM LOSING MY BALANCE!

OH NO!

TANTRI... WHAT?

YOUR HIGHNESS!

YIPPEE!

SPLASH

HELP!

I'LL GO GET HELP, YOUR HIGHNESS. DON'T WORRY, THE LIFE JACKET WILL HELP YOU...

...DROWN.

GASP!

SUDDENLY –

EH?

WHAT THE...?

FLAP

FLAP

TANTRI, LOOK! I CAN SWIM!

ER...WHERE DID YOU LEARN SWIMMING?

I DIDN'T LEARN SWIMMING, TANTRI. I AM A NATURAL!

I SEE. YOU WON'T BE NEEDING HELP THEN.

HOOJA SWAM BACK TO THE SHORE.

YOU CAN KEEP MY LIFE JACKET, TANTRI. I DON'T NEED IT ANYMORE. I AM A NATURAL SWIMMER, AREN'T I?

LATER –

LET'S GO TO THE FUN FAIR AT THE BEACH THIS EVENING. THERE ARE LOTS OF EXCITING SHOPS THERE.

HMM.

THERE IS STILL SOME TIME BEFORE WE GET BACK HOME. I CAN TRY SOMETHING ELSE.

THAT EVENING AT THE FUN FAIR –

I SEEM TO HAVE LOST FAT FACE. THIS SHOP LOOKS INTERESTING. LET ME CHECK IT OUT.

UNEXPECTED GIFTS

WOULD YOU LIKE TO LOOK AT OUR NORMAL GIFTS OR SOMETHING... UNEXPECTED?

ER...A GIFT BUT A LITTLE UNEXPECTED ONE...LIKE A TRICK, YOU KNOW.

31

HMM. YOU LIKE PLAYING TRICKS TOO, EH? HOW ABOUT THIS? IT'S MY PERSONAL FAVOURITE.

A CAMERA? WHAT'S UNEXPECTED ABOUT THAT?

OH IT IS, DEAR SIR. CLICK A PICTURE AND THE PERSON YOU ARE PHOTOGRAPHING WILL BE STUNNED FOR AT LEAST HALF AN HOUR.

OOH!

AFTER I STUN JELLY BELLY I CAN THROW HIM OFF THE CLIFF.

OBVIOUSLY, TANTRI BOUGHT THE CAMERA AND RUSHED BACK TO THE RESORT.

THERE YOU ARE, YOUR HIGHNESS. I LOST YOU AT THE FUN FAIR. SEE WHAT I'VE BOUGHT.

THERE YOU ARE, TANTRI! NOW JUST STAND RIGHT THERE FOR A MOMENT, THE ANGLE IS PERFECT.

SAY CHEESE, MY DEAR TANTRI!

HUH?!

CLICK

IT WORKED! SUCH A NEAT TRICK, DON'T YOU THINK, TANTRI? I'M JUST PAYING YOU BACK FOR OUR TRICK THIS MORNING.

NAUGHTY TANTRI, I KNOW YOU PUSHED ME ON PURPOSE SO THAT I COULD LEARN SWIMMING. SO I THOUGHT I'D PLAY A TRICK ON YOU TOO! DON'T WORRY, IT LASTS FOR ONLY HALF AN HOUR.

GRR! THAT'S TWO PLANS GONE BUST IN ONE DAY!

Tantri the Mantri
Boomerang Botch-Up

Illustrations: Prachi Killekar

HOOJA OPENED THE BOX.

WHAT IS THIS? IT'S GOT SUCH A FUNNY SHAPE, TANTRI.

THIS...OH, IT'S JUST A PIECE OF WOOD. IT MUST HAVE COME HERE BY MISTAKE.

OH! I'LL OPEN ANOTHER ONE.

CHUBBY DOESN'T EVEN KNOW A BOOMERANG WHEN HE SEES ONE! THIS WILL HELP ME GET RID OF HOOJA ONCE AND FOR ALL!

THAT EVENING, TANTRI ROUNDED UP DUSHTABUDDHI AND KUBUDDHI.

DO YOU NEED ANOTHER OF MY BRILLIANT INVENTIONS, TANTRI? THIS LAUGHING POWDER WILL MAKE HOOJA GIGGLE UNTIL HE GASPS....

OH, I'VE HAD ENOUGH OF YOUR SILLY INVENTIONS! I FINALLY HAVE A MASTER WEAPON TO GET RID OF HOOJA.

WHAT?! THAT PIECE OF WOOD?!

WELL, IT WOULD BE PERFECT FOR BONKING HOOJA ON THE HEAD. I LIKE YOUR IDEA, TANTRI.

WILL YOU FOOLS JUST LISTEN? THIS IS A BOOMERANG. WHEN YOU THROW IT...

...IT FLIES TOWARDS YOUR TARGET...

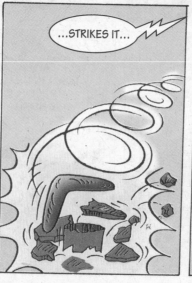

...STRIKES IT...

...AND THEN COMES BACK TO YOUR HAND.

34

WOW! THAT'S AN EXCELLENT WEAPON.

YES, GOOD TRICK, TANTRI!

I KNOW! THE BEST PART IS THAT HOOJA WON'T KNOW WHAT HIT HIM!

NOW, LISTEN CAREFULLY. I'M GOING TO TAKE HOOJA FOR A WALK IN THE GARDEN TOMORROW.

YES, YOU MUST. HOOJA HAS BEEN GETTING EXTRA CHUBBY LATELY.

YOU FOOL! THE PLAN IS TO GET RID OF HIM, NOT TAKE HIM OUT FOR FRESH AIR AND EXERCISE!

OH!

SILLY FELLOW!

ONCE WE'RE IN THE GARDEN, I WANT YOU TO THROW THE BOOMERANG AT HIM. THAT WILL BE THE END OF THE ROLY-POLY ROYAL NUISANCE!

THE BOOMERANG WILL FLY BACK TO US AFTER KNOCKING HOOJA OUT, SO THERE WON'T BE ANY PROOF OF THE CRIME.

AH, YOU'VE UNDERSTOOD MY PLAN AT LAST. WE'LL DO IT TOMORROW.

TANTRI, IT LOOKS LIKE THIS TIME, YOU WILL ACTUALLY SUCCEED.

AND IF YOU DON'T, AT LEAST YOU AND HOOJA WILL GET SOME EXERCISE.

GRRR... DUSHTABUDDHI, WILL YOU PLEASE SHUT UP!

35

THE NEXT DAY —

WHAT A GOOD IDEA TO WALK IN THE GARDEN, TANTRI.

I ALWAYS HAVE GOOD IDEAS, SIRE...

...ALTHOUGH NONE OF THEM HAS HELPED ME GET RID OF YOU YET!

DUSHTABUDDHI AND KUBUDDHI WERE HIDING BEHIND THE TREES WITH THE BOOMERANG.

THEY'RE HERE. THROW IT!

BUT JUST THEN —

TANTRI, LOOK AT THIS LITTLE BIRD! ISN'T IT SWEET!

THE BOOMERANG SAILED OVER HOOJA'S HEAD AND —

THWACK

AAAAH!

TANTRI! TANTRI! WHERE ARE YOU?!

TANTRI'S PLANS ALWAYS BACKFIRE, DON'T THEY?

PLAY, CREATE and SHARE on www.TinkleOnline.com

PLAY

Play games with your favourite Tinkle Toons – Suppandi & Shikari Shambu. Solve fun-filled puzzles, quizzes and more.

CREATE

Create your own avatars, write stories & draw toons!

SHARE

Share stories, fun facts and exchange virtual gifts with your friends.

www.TinkleOnline.com – India's first fully-moderated destination site for kids

Tantri The Mantri
The Big Bang

Story:
Jubel D'Cruz

Script:
Anomita Guha

Illustrations:
Prachi Killekar

TANTRI WAS IN A BAD MOOD.

MY DREAM OF BECOMING KING WILL NEVER COME TRUE.

WHY THE LONG FACE, TANTRI? WHAT'S THE MATTER?

OH, I'M FED UP OF WAITING FOR THINGS TO HAPPEN! I WISH I COULD SEE INTO THE FUTURE.

WHY DON'T YOU GO TO AN ASTROLOGER? HE MAY BE ABLE TO HELP.

AN ASTROLOGER? GOOD IDEA, HOKI POKI!

GO MEET SALUNI THE SEER. I'VE HEARD THAT ALL HIS PREDICTIONS COME TRUE.

THE NEXT DAY —

WELCOME, TANTRI! IT'S GOOD TO SEE YOU.

HOW... HOW DID YOU KNOW MY NAME?!

AAH! I KNOW EVERYTHING... I SEE EVERYTHING. I CAN SENSE THAT YOU ARE A VERY AMBITIOUS MAN, TANTRI.

YES, YES... ALL-KNOWING ONE!

YOU WANT TO REACH THE VERY TOP.

THIS FELLOW EVEN KNOWS THAT I WANT TO TAKE HOOJA'S PLACE AS KING!

WELL, I CAN TELL YOU THAT WHATEVER YOU PLAN WILL GO OFF WITH A BIG BANG!

REALLY? ON THE BRINK OF SUCCESS, FINALLY!

I GUARANTEE IT.

MAY YOUR WORDS BE AS TRUE AS THE SUN RISING IN THE EAST!

TANTRI WAS ON HIS WAY TO THE PALACE WHEN HE MET GYANI THE SCIENTIST..

GOOD..BUT I'M VERY BUSY. I'M WORKING ON A PROJECT.

TANTRI, HOW ARE YOU?

OH, THEN I WON'T KEEP YOU FROM YOUR WORK. BUT I'VE GOT SOME VERY GOOD NEWS.

YOU DO? THEN TELL ME QUICKLY, GYANI. I'M IN A HURRY.

WELL, I'VE JUST INVENTED ...NY DEVICE THAT CAN ...LOW UP THINGS. IT'S SO SMALL THAT IT CAN BE HIDDEN ANYWHERE.

WHY, GYANI, THAT'S CLEVER OF YOU. GIVE IT TO ME. HERE'S AN ADVANCE.

NOW MY PROJECT CAN REALLY TAKE OFF!

IT CAN?

39

TANTRI LOST NO TIME IN PUTTING HIS PLAN INTO ACTION.

WHAT ARE YOU CARRYING IN THAT BAG, TANTRI? IS IT A GIFT FOR HOOJA?

WELL, YOU COULD SAY HE'LL HAVE A BLAST WITH IT!

I'LL PLANT THIS IN HOOJA'S TV SET. HE'LL SWITCH IT ON TO WATCH HIS FAVOURITE SHOW AND **BANG** .. HE'LL BE BLOWN TO BITS!

THE NEXT DAY—

HOOJA MUST BE HISTORY BY NOW! SOON, THE CROWN WILL BE MINE!

BUT WHEN TANTRI ARRIVED AT THE PALACE—

OH, TANTRI. YOU'VE JUST MISSED A GOOD TV SHOW.

HE'S ALIVE!

UH...YES, YOUR MAJESTY. MISSING OUT ON OPPORTUNITIES IS BECOMING A HABIT WITH ME.

THAT STUPID GYANI HAS FAILED ME! HIS DEVICE WAS COMPLETELY USELESS.

TANTRI RETURNED HOME GRUMPILY.

WHAT ROTTEN LUCK!

TANTRI, YOU'RE HOME! THERE'S A SURPRISE WAITING FOR YOU.

WHY, YOU'VE BOUGHT A NEW TV SET!

OH, I DIDN'T BUY IT.

HUH?!

IT'S A GIFT FROM ....

CLICK

BANG

LATER –

TANTRI! THANK GOD, YOU'RE ALIVE!

ONCE AGAIN, YOU'VE SAVED MY LIFE, TANTRI.

WHO WOULD HAVE THOUGHT THERE WAS A BOMB CONCEALED IN THE TV SET I SENT YOU?!

WELL, MY PLANS DID GO OFF WITH A BANG!

???

HUMPH... I HATE ASTROLOGERS!

???

Tantri The Mantri
in
The Cave of Dreams

Script: Luis Fernandes
Illustrations: Prachi Killekar

A LETTER FOR YOU.

IT'S FROM ALIBABA AND CO. MY ALIBABA CAVE IS READY!

WHAT'S AN ALIBABA CAVE?

IT'S AN ANTI-THEFT, ARTIFICIAL CAVE BUILT IN A SECRET LOCATION.

EACH CAVE COMES WITH ITS OWN SECRET PASSWORD. THE CAVE OPENS AND CLOSES WHEN THE PASSWORD IS SHOUTED OUT.

WHAT WILL THEY THINK OF NEXT?

TANTRI GOES TO INSPECT HIS CAVE.

ACCORDING TO THIS MAP THEY SENT, IT SHOULD BE SOMEWHERE HERE.

AH, THAT MUST BE IT!

NOW, WHAT'S THE PASSWORD? LET'S SEE... IT IS...

...KRUNG THEP THOOP!

DRRRR -RRRR

NICE ... NICE!

NEAT AND COMPACT. IT COULD EASILY HOLD ALL MY PRECIOUS STONES AND MY JARS OF GOLD...

...A MODEST TREASURE ACTUALLY WHEN YOU THINK OF THE TREASURE THAT HOOJA HAS!

IF ONLY I COULD DETHRONE HOOJA AND TAKE HIS PLACE! A THOUSAND ALI BABA CAVES WOULD NOT BE ENOUGH TO HOLD MY TREASURES THEN!

BUT WHAT'S THE USE OF DREAMING? HE HAS SURVIVED ALL MY TRAPS! HE'S LAZY, INCOMPETENT, CARELESS, FORGETFUL... BUT HE'S LUCKY!

HEY, WAIT A MINUTE! WHAT DID I SAY? FORGETFUL! AH, NOW THAT GIVES ME AN IDEA! A BRILLIANT IDEA, IN FACT!

ALL I HAVE TO DO IS BRING HIM HERE AND CLOSE THE DOOR ON HIM.

HE WOULD NEVER REMEMBER THE PASSWORD EVEN IF HE HEARD ME SAY IT A THOUSAND TIMES. HE WOULD BE LOCKED IN FOREVER!

OH, WHAT JOY!

AND SO — YOU WANT ME TO COME AND SEE YOUR CAVE? BUT I'VE HUNDREDS OF ALI BABA CAVES MYSELF, TANTRI! WHAT'S SPECIAL ABOUT YOURS?

WHAT'S SPECIAL ABOUT MY CAVE?

ER ... WELL, IT'S LOCATED IN A BREATHTAKINGLY BEAUTIFUL PART OF HARABHARA FOREST!

IT'S SO QUIET AND PEACEFUL THERE, YOU CAN ALMOST HEAR THE FLOWERS BREATHING! IT'S THE IDEAL PLACE TO GO TO IF YOU WANT TO GET AWAY FROM THE HUSTLE AND BUSTLE OF THE CITY.

BUT I DON'T WANT TO GET AWAY FROM THE HUSTLE AND BUSTLE...

...IN FACT, I LIKE HUSTLE AND BUSTLE! I FEEL ENERGISED WHEN I SEE PEOPLE HUSTLING AND BUSTLING AROUND ME.

YOU WOULD, YOU FAT FROG!

QUIET AND LONELY PLACES REMIND ME OF TOMBS AND GRAVEYARDS.

BUT YOU'VE GOT TO COME TO MY TOMB ... I ...I MEAN CAVE, YOUR HIGHNESS!

PROSPERITY WILL COME TO ME ONLY IF YOU INAUGURATE IT!

SO THAT'S IT!

YOU FEEL SOME OF MY LUCK WILL RUB OFF ON YOU IF I COME TO YOUR CAVE? WELL, I'LL CERTAINLY COME BUT NOT FOR ANOTHER TWO DAYS AT LEAST.

I'M READING A BOOK THAT COULD TRANSFORM MY LIFE AND .....

WHAT ABOUT MONDAY?

MONDAY IS AN AUSPICIOUS DAY TO START SOMETHING NEW.

LIKE THE BEGINNING OF MY REIGN ... HEH-HEH!

WELL, I'LL FINISH THE BOOK BY SUNDAY... YOU REALLY MUST READ IT AFTERWARDS, TANTRI. IT COULD CHANGE YOUR LIFE FOREVER!

THAT'S WHAT I'M TRYING TO DO. I MEAN, MONDAY IS FIXED, THEN?

LET'S SLIP OUT QUIETLY, YOUR HIGHNESS. I DON'T WANT ANYONE TO KNOW I'VE GOT AN ALIBABA CAVE, NOR WOULD I LIKE ANYONE TO KNOW WHERE IT IS LOCATED.

TANTRI THE MANTRI HAS HATCHED ANOTHER DASTARDLY PLOT TO GET RID OF RAJA HOOJA AND TAKE OVER THE THRONE. WILL HE SUCCEED? LET'S FOLLOW THE TWO MEN AS THEY MAKE THEIR WAY THROUGH HARABHARA FOREST EARLY THE FOLLOWING MONDAY.

IT'S SO REFRESHING TO BE OUT SO EARLY IN THE MORNING, DON'T YOU THINK SO, YOUR HIGHNESS?

I DON'T THINK HE THINKS SO.

ZZZZ

AFTER AN UNEVENTFUL JOURNEY —

MY ALIBABA CAVE, YOUR HIGHNESS!

I WAS DREAMING OF THE WAY THE BOOK HAD TRANSFORMED MY LIFE WHEN YOU WOKE ME!

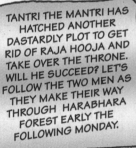

HERE, I BROUGHT YOU THE BOOK ... READ IT CAREFULLY.

I WILL, I WILL!

AND HERE'S SOMETHING YOU COULD KEEP IN YOUR CAVE TO START WITH.

A DIAMOND AS BIG AS AN EGG! YOUR GENEROSITY IS BOUNDLESS, YOUR HIGHNESS.

NOW, LET'S GET INTO THE CAVE!

NO HURRY! AS YOU SAY, IT'S BEAUTIFUL HERE.

NOW WHERE'S THAT PASSWORD ...AH, HERE IT IS...

KRUNG THEP THOOP!

DRRR-DRRR

WELCOME TO MY HUMBLE TREASURE HOUSE.

NICE AND COMPACT ... BUT DOESN'T THE CAVE CLOSE ONCE YOU'VE ENTERED?

IT CLOSES AUTOMATICALLY AFTER TEN MINUTES.

IF YOU WANT IT TO CLOSE BEFORE THAT YOU'VE TO SAY THE PASSWORD.

YOU LOOK AROUND, I'LL SEE IF THE HORSES ARE ALL RIGHT.

I'LL COME WITH YOU.

NO, NO, DON'T COME WITH ME! IT'S TOO COLD AND WINDY OUTSIDE.

I'LL CLOSE THE DOOR ... YOU CAN WATCH IT CLOSING FROM THE INSIDE.

KRUNG THEP THOOP

DRAA-DRAA

OOPS ... THERE GOES THE PASSWORD!

BUT I DON'T THINK I'LL EVER NEED IT AGAIN!

HE'S LOCKED IN FOREVER! AND SOON I'LL TAKE HIS PLACE ON THE THRONE.

I WONDER WHAT THE BOOK HE WAS RAVING ABOUT IS ABOUT ....

WHAT!

30 DAYS TO A POWERFUL MEMORY!

COULD HE HAVE DEVELOPED A SUPER MEMORY AFTER READING THIS BOOK? IF HE HAS, THEN HE'LL REMEMBER THE PASSWORD!

I'D BETTER GO BACK AND CHECK!

A BIG DISAPPOINTMENT AWAITS TANTRI.

HE IS GONE!

ALL MY PLANS HAVE GONE AWRY AGAIN!

I'LL KEEP THE DIAMOND HE GAVE ME INSIDE AND HURRY AFTER HIM.

IT WON'T BE HARD TO CONVINCE THE SIMPLETON THAT I WAS JUST TESTING HIS MEMORY. IN FACT, HE MUST HAVE ALREADY COME TO THAT CONCLUSION.

TANTRI THE MANTRI in

The Hic-O-Virus

Illustrations:
Prachi Killekar

WHAT ARE YOU DOING, TANTRI?

JUST CHECKING THE NEWS...

...WHO KNOWS? FAT FACE HOOJA MIGHT HAVE BEEN ATTACKED BY AN UNKNOWN ENEMY!

HMMM... NO SUCH LUCK!

BUT WHAT IS THIS MYSTERIOUS DISEASE THAT HAS HIT SARDIPUR?

A MYSTERIOUS DISEASE THAT CAUSES A PERSON TO HICCUP CONTINUOUSLY IS SWEEPING THROUGH SARDIPUR.

NO ONE HAS BEEN ABLE TO FIND A CURE FOR IT THOUGH THE GREAT DR NALLABUDDHI HAS IDENTIFIED THE VIRUS RESPONSIBLE FOR IT. HE HAS NAMED IT THE HIC-O-VIRUS.

NOW, WOULDN'T IT BE GREAT IF MY GOOD FRIEND HOOJA WERE TO CONTRACT THIS DELIGHTFUL DISEASE?

YOU CAN'T HAVE A KING WHO HICCUPS CONTINUOUSLY. HE'LL HAVE TO GIVE UP THE THRONE AND THEN...HEH HEH....

TANTRI PAID DR NALLABUDDHI A VISIT THE VERY NEXT DAY.

DR NALLABUDDHI, PLEASE TELL ME HOW THE HIC-O-VIRUS SPREADS.

THROUGH INFECTED FOOD, MR TANTRI. THE PERSON STARTS HICCUPING AS SOON HE TAKES A BITE OF THE FOOD AND DOESN'T STOP UNTIL HE BECOMES UNCONSCIOUS.

TRING TRING

EXCUSE ME, I HAVE TO ANSWER THE PHONE.

TAKE YOUR TIME.

TRING TRING

AHA! A HIC-O-VIRUS SAMPLE...PERFECT!

HIC-O-VIRU

GREETINGS, SIR. WHAT CAN THIS HUMBLE COOK DO FOR YOU?

WHICH IS THE KING'S PLATE?

THAT ONE.

YOU MAY LEAVE FOR NOW. I WILL TAKE THE KING'S LUNCH TO HIM.

HERE GOES...HICCUP AWAY, FAT FACE! I'LL ADD SOME TO THE RICE AS WELL TO MAKE SURE!

LET'S HAVE LUNCH, YOUR HIGHNESS.

MY LOYAL TANTRI ALWAYS MAKES SURE I HAVE MORE FOOD THAN HE DOES...

...IT IS SO UNFAIR! I AM HEALTHY AND HE IS SO THIN!

THERE, NOW OUR PORTIONS ARE EQUAL.

EAT, TANTRI. I WON'T EAT A MORSEL TILL YOU DO.

OH, ALL RIGHT.

HIC

HIC

HIC

HIC
HIC
HIC

WHAT'S WRONG, TANTRI?

SWOON

TANTRI HAS FAINTED! CALL DR NALLABUDDHI, QUICK!

IT'S THE HIC-O-VIRUS, BUT NOT TO WORRY, SIRE. I HAVE FOUND THE CURE. HE WILL BE ALL RIGHT IN NO TIME.

THANK GOODNESS!

I WONDER HOW HE CONTRACTED IT, THOUGH.

HIC

HIC
HIC

TANTRI THE MANTRI
in
THE MAZE

Script:
Jennifer Alphonso

Illustrations:
Prachi Killekar

HOOJA IS LAZY BUT HE LOVES A CHALLENGE!

WHY DON'T I BUILD A SET OF TRAPS - A MAZE FROM WHICH HE CAN NEVER GET OUT ALIVE!

AND SO —

I WANT YOU TO CONSTRUCT A HUGE MAZE IN THE JUNGLE THAT IS FULL OF FALSE LEADS, DEAD ENDS AND TRAP DOORS. THIS WILL BE ONE OF THE ATTRACTIONS OF THE ANNUAL ROYAL GAMES.

MAKE SURE THE TRAP DOORS ARE WELL COVERED SO THAT ONLY THE TRULY BRAVE AND WISE WILL BE ABLE TO GET ACROSS.

UNDER THIS TRAP DOOR, YOU WILL PUT HUNGRY CROCODILES.

UNDER THIS TRAP DOOR, YOU WILL PUT POISONOUS SPIDERS.

UNDER THIS TRAP DOOR, PLACE A POOL OF HUNGRY PIRANHA!

THE HIGHLIGHT OF THIS YEAR'S ANNUAL ROYAL GAMES: THE MAN WHO EMERGES FROM THE MAZE WILL BE DECLARED THE BRAVEST MAN IN THE KINGDOM!

THE MAZE IS THE TALK OF THE TOWN —

TANTRI, THE IDEA OF THE MAZE IS EXCELLENT. I WANT TO BE THE FIRST TO TRY IT.

OF COURSE SIRE, YOUR WISH IS MY COMMAND!

I NEVER IMAGINED THIS WOULD BE SO EASY!

HEH HEH HEH!

THE DAY OF THE MAZE EVENT —

TIME ME, TANTRI.

CERTAINLY SIRE!

55

ONLY ONE OF HIS VICTIMS EVER MADE IT BACK HOME...

WATER... (GASP)... WATER...

..HE WENT TO THE POLICE, AND DEZERT WAS ARRESTED AND SENT TO PRISON FOR 14 YEARS.

HE HAS SERVED SEVEN YEARS OF THAT SENTENCE AND NOW HE BEGS FOR FREEDOM...

... AND I THINK I'LL GIVE IT TO HIM! FOR A SMALL FAVOUR, OF COURSE...

THE WICKED TANTRI HAS HATCHED YET ANOTHER DIABOLICAL PLAN TO GET RID OF HIS MASTER, KING HOOJA, SO THAT HE CAN GRAB THE THRONE.

YOU WANT ME TO COME TO THE DESERT WITH YOU, TANTRI? BUT WHY? AS YOU KNOW, THIS IS A VERY BUSY PERIOD FOR ME.

THE HOT-AIR BALLOON ASSOCIATION IS GOING TO DISPLAY A VARIETY OF HOT-AIR BALLOONS NEXT WEEK, ON THE OCCASION OF THE HOT-AIR BALLOON FESTIVAL, AND...

IF YOU ASK ME THOSE HOT-AIR BALLOON PEOPLE ARE ALL FULL OF GAS!

... AND AS I'M THE PRESIDENT OF THE ASSOCIATION...

(GULP)

I HAVE TO BE PRESENT!

NATURALLY! THOSE HOT-AIR BALLOON PEOPLE DESERVE A MEDAL FOR THE GREAT WORK THEY'RE DOING!

61

THE DESERT SHOULD BE ENJOYED IN SOLITUDE. THIS IS OUR GUIDE, DEZERT RHET.

GLAD TO MEET YOU MR DESERT RAT!

ER... IT'S DEZERT RHET...

DID I MISPRONOUNCE? OH, DEAR! I HAVE A HABIT OF MISPRONOUNCING NAMES...

SORRY MR RAT!

RHET! RHET!

OUR GUIDE IS A VERY QUIET MAN, I MUST SAY. SEEMS TO BE LOST IN THOUGHT.

A DESERT IS A GOOD PLACE TO GET LOST... IN THOUGHT, I MEAN.

WELL, I WISH HE WOULD FIND HIMSELF AND SAY: 'LET'S STOP FOR LUNCH'!

WE'RE ON A PICNIC AFTER ALL, AND WHAT'S A PICNIC WITHOUT LUNCH?

ABSOLUTELY RIGHT!

I WONDER IF WE'RE FAR ENOUGH IN THE DESERT TO LOSE HIM.

I'LL ASK DEZERT...

...ER... DEZERT... ???!!!

WHERE'S HE! DEZERT HAS DESERTED US!! HE'S GONE!

NO NEED TO PANIC. PERHAPS HE HAS GONE BEHIND ONE OF THOSE BOULDERS FOR PERSONAL REASONS.

65

66

TANTRI THE MANTRI
in 'Shark Attack'

Script: Anomita Guha
Illustrations: Prachi Killekar
Colouring: Rajesh Phatak

TANTRI WAS FEELING HAPPY FOR ONCE –

I'M GOING ON A HOLIDAY! I'LL BE FAR AWAY FROM HOOJA AND HIS FAT FACE FOR TWO WHOLE WEEKS! YIPPEE!

TANTRI!

WHY DO YOU HAVE YOUR BAGS PACKED? WHERE ARE YOU GOING?

OH, ONLY FOR A SHORT VACATION TO THE ISLANDS, SIRE! I'LL BE BACK BEFORE YOU KNOW IT!

WHY, THAT'S AN EXCELLENT IDEA! I NEED A BREAK FROM RUNNING THE KINGDOM ...I'LL COME WITH YOU!

Y...YOU WILL?! ER..LUCKY ME!

AT THE ISLAND –

THIS IS SO RELAXING, TANTRI! JUST THE SUN, THE SAND, THE SEA...AND US!

ER...NOT JUST US, YOUR HIGHNESS!

YOU FORGOT THE ROYAL UMBRELLA CARRIER...

...THE ROYAL LIFE GUARDS...

...AND THE ROYAL SHOWER SYSTEM!

YOU'RE RIGHT AS USUAL, TANTRI! THIS IS LIKE BEING BACK AT THE PALACE, SURROUNDED BY MY ENTIRE STAFF!

I WISH I COULD GO ON A PROPER VACATION WITHOUT ALL THIS FUSS!

MAYBE YOU CAN, YOUR MAJESTY!

ALL YOU HAVE TO DO IS DISGUISE YOURSELF SO THAT NO ONE CAN RECOGNIZE YOU AS KING HOOJA!

EXCELLENT IDEA! I'LL DO IT AT ONCE!

70

SPLASH!

SH...SH...SH...SHARKS! THEY'VE HAD A TASTE OF HOOJA AND NOW THEY WANT ME!

(SPLUTTER!)...I HAVE TO GET AWAY!

TAAAANTRI!

!!!

WHEEE!

HOW CLEVER OF YOU TO ARRANGE A SWIM WITH THE DOLPHINS FOR ME, TANTRI!

(SPLUTTER)... DOLPHINS FOR YOU...

...BUT I'M BEING CHASED BY A SHARK! HELP!